Memory Matters

117 William Hilton Parkway

Hilton Head Island, SC 29926

(843) 842-6688

www.memory-matters.org

Meet Me Where I Am

An uplifting collection of creative expressions

Edited by Lynne Cope Hummell

Lydia Inglett Ltd. Publishing
Award-winning publishers of elegant books

memorymatters is an award-winning, nationally recognized, community-based, non-profit organization which strives to be a center of excellence for persons with Alzheimer's and all forms of dementia and their families, by providing daycare programs, support services and education in a compassionate and dignified manner.
www.memory-matters.org

Proceeds from the sale of this book will benefit the community of caregivers
and their loved ones served by Memory Matters.
Memory Matters gratefully acknowledges the contributions of the Camera Club of Hilton Head Island, SC

Meet Me Where I Am

ISBN: 978-1-938417-25-2
© 2015 Copyright Memory Matters

To order additional books, learn more about our pursuit of excellence and join our community: www.memory-matters.org

Memory Matters
117 William Hilton Pkwy., Hilton Head, SC 29926
Mailing Address: P.O. Box 22330, Hilton Head, SC 29925-2330
843-842-6688 office, 843-681-5522 fax
info@memory-matters.org

 Published by Lydia Inglett Ltd. Publishing
www.lydiainglett.com
www.starbooks.biz
301 Central Ave. #181
Hilton Head Island, SC 29926
info@starbooks.biz

To order more copies of this or any of our books, visit our on-line bookstore

www.STARBOOKS.biz
The place for beautiful, thoughtful gift books

Lydia Inglett Ltd. Publishing
Award-winning publishers of elegant books

In memory of our loved ones who traveled the journey of dementia,

and

In honor of those still making their way,

this book of reflections is dedicated to the caregivers

who were and are traveling alongside

to comfort,

to smile,

to embrace,

to hope,

to love.

Coming Home by William Bosley

Introduction

This book is a rich, unique tapestry created with threads of hope, humor, love, faith and compassion that hopefully will inspire others who give of themselves relentlessly in their role as caregivers. Dementia care may, at times, seem to unravel the threads of family life as caregivers navigate this difficult journey.

Imagine a mountain to climb. The mountain is simply there, but those who must climb it each have unique experiences, challenges and attitudes about their journeys. To some the climb is arduous and overwhelming. To others the climb is not a choice, but a requirement of circumstance. Some prepare well, others do not. Some stop to gaze at the magnificent views, others see only rocks, cliffs and obstacles. For all, the journey is hard. The miracle is that there can be joy, there must be hope, and mistakes and loss do not have to define and consume you.

The climb is exhausting, but at the summit is a 360° vista that offers an amazing, fresh perspective and a new world view.

This book is a vision created by caregivers who conquered the summit. They decided to share the joy, humor, and wisdom that they gained through their personal ascent.

> – Edwina Hoyle
> Executive Director, Memory Matters

Reflection & Transmittance by Albert Heacox

Welcoming the First One In

My mom was the first participant of Alzheimer's Respite & Resource, as Memory Matters was originally called.

Though I knew all about the program as well as the people working there, I was still a little nervous when I drove her to St. Luke's Church on the opening day. I knew in my heart that bringing her there was a good thing, particularly for my dad, who needed some respite. However, I wasn't sure how Mom would react to this new experience in a foreign place.

I remember walking my mom to the door and being greeted by the director and standing there as my mom was gently led into the room and introduced to the volunteers. She hugged some of them as if they were her dear friends.

As I watched her, tears welled up in me.

My mom had been my dad's "right hand girl" in his medical practice throughout his career, greeting and assisting the patients and taking care of the financial responsibilities. She also had been president of the Nassau County and New York State Women's Medical Societies.

That day, though her illness was eating away her memory, she was still able to express her love for humanity.

My dear mother loved going to her "club," where she would sing and dance and paint her pictures until she could no longer live at home. Somewhere from deep down, her kindness and love affected the volunteers who helped her, because those who I run into still speak so lovingly of her.

– Barbara Marcinkowski

HAPPY

Sunshine.

Bright, warm, light

Uplifting

Makes everything grow and glow

YOU'RE ALIVE!

Let's go play golf!

(But it won't improve your score.)

Sunshine.

– Participants in Memory Matters Connections Class, 2014

Sun Flowers by Albert Heacox

Cypress Gardens by Albert Heacox

What Is It Like?

What is it like?
What's it like to not remember?
What's it like when you know you are failing?
What's it like to pretend all is well?
What's it like?
How we wish
We could get inside the mind
And make it change direction.
How we wish.
What's it like for the caregiver?
This we know.
How do we cope with the pain?
Memory Matters!

– Betsy Pehrson

Azalea by Albert Heacox

Rip Tide at Dockside by William Bosley

Flowing Water by Albert Heacox

You Gotta Laugh!

What do you do when you are the caregiver and you break your leg? You do your best.

I borrowed a wheelchair and he pushed while I held the leash to walk the dog. It was a lovely "outing" until we approached the house and he walked inside, leaving me behind in the road!

Knowing he would forget me, I used my strength to push the chair up over the curb. Whoops! The wheelchair flipped backwards in slow motion. There I was with my head in the road and my leg in a cast looking like a mast without a sail.

Fortunately a neighbor came jogging by and asked if I needed help. Ya think?

You've gotta laugh!

– Jeffra Emmerich

Roller Relics by Vicki Reilly

My mother had Alzheimer's disease and one day my sister was visiting her when our mother's husband wasn't home. The phone rang, and someone obviously asked for "Mr. or Mrs. Tuve." Mother replied, "Neither of us is here right now," and hung up the phone.

I've used that line for years when receiving an unwanted call!

– Susan Reynolds

The Prize

Losing you slowly
A drip of water from a drain
Unable to catch it as it slips through my fingers
What you are this morning
Where you live
The day
The season
Gone
Yet somehow you still hold tight to the memory
Of the ring you'd hidden in that box of Cheerios
A prize that I'd find when you asked
Me to marry you

– Nancy Ball

Peaceful Falls by Fiona Grygiel

Hope

Life's journey wends its way
Thick and thin it trucks along
We see our changes through.
Confidence runs high—inspired by spirit.

Faulters worm their way in.
But who does not love the rush of confidence?
Who does not hate the slug of despair?
We must battle despair, hate it, defeat it!

Seeing her tears, hearing her cry breaks my heart.
Better laughter, better smiles, better by far.
Vulnerable is she, yet strong still.
I see her (and sometimes me) stumble and rise up, yet again.

– T. P. Foster

15

Vermont Fog by Donna Varner

Reflection by Edith Wood

You greet me with a smile, hugs and even a kiss.

We walk a little, holding hands, and sit. I wonder what you're thinking.

Then you get up and leave—saying nothing. It's the end of the visit.
It hurts, and we say it's okay. Never to understand.

Just let it go!

– Anonymous

Foggy Morning by Edith Wood

Mr. Blue Eyes by Carol Clemens

Preening by Edith Wood

Your Next Buddy by Carol Clemens

Happy Dance by Suzi Huisman

Nice Catch by Carol Clemens

Green Heron by Carol Clemens

Which Way Do I Go by Carol Clemens

Tricolored Heron by Kendra Natter

Take the Day

A reminder that age is not to be feared

Nibble the ice cream small bites at a time

Sit back and relax

There is always tomorrow

No time for gloom or sorrow

Take the day with eyes open wide

Sit back and take pride that numbers do not matter

Just keep hope and put cares aside

No time for gloom and doom

Take the day

With eyes wide open

Sit back and take pride.

– Selma Lipsius, Summer 2009

Windowbox, Charleston by Donna Varner

Windowbox, Vieux Québec by Donna Varner

Memory

Memory, memory

Days that used to be

I used to think it could happen

To anyone but me

But now that I've passed the big 9-0

Something had to go

And I'm glad

It's only memory

– Selma Lipsius, 2007

20

Just Go With It

"We went shopping yesterday."

"Who?"

"Mother and I. They took all my money."

"Who?"

"You know, the one with the red hair. The fat one, and those others."

So go our conversations. Not long ago I would have said, "Stop talking about your mother. She's dead. Been dead for 30 years. You know that. Your mother doesn't shop. She's dead."

No longer do I say things such as, "You know that's not your brother. It's your husband," or "This IS your house! You lived on Myrtle Avenue 50 years ago. Remember?"

Hard as it has been, I have learned to dive right into the fantasy life she is living.

"Ah, yes, Myrtle Avenue. Tell me about the house," I say. Once I let go of the struggle to keep the smart, funny, organized, engaging mother I knew, and acknowledged that she would never be that person again, my life changed.

The battle was over.

Now I step into different roles. One day I might be Aunt Aggie who gave Mother the china head doll on her 6th birthday. On occasion, I play the part of her friend, Lovey Garrigan. Together we rode the DeKalb Avenue subway to lunch at the Automat.

Over the years she has addressed me as her mother-in-law, neighbor, and teacher—the evil Sister Mary Grace.

I've met people from Mother's past that I never would have known and we've shared adventures that enriched my life. Losing pieces of my mother, day by day, is tragic, but by adopting my mantra, "just go with it," I opened a window into her past, and my life has been enriched.

– Mary Dempsey

Benches by James Hartley Smith

Caregiver's Journey

Climb …

Keep moving …
Watch your step.

Find "refreshment" where you can …
Cool waters flow to soothe your weary soul.

Absorb every good moment to nourish and cleanse the Self.

Don't look back …
For Time has moved on.

If you raise your eyes from the rocky crags …
You will see the Light.

Always direct your gaze upward …
And the Light will Brighten.

Concentrate on the Forward Glow
And find your "Song of Knowing" to Sing.

Reach as you Climb …
Trusting in the Unseen Hand.

You are NOT alone on this Journey.

– Wanda Eastham

Graces of Slumber

Dark grace stealthily stalks my brain.
In the wee hours like sullen rain,
Brings worries of things left undone;
Concerns of lost atonement.

An avalanche of crises hits, rumbles,
… as a wrecking ball to my temples.
Does my account have enough;
Not of money, but of bright grace?

Bright grace will come yet again
As dawn breaks in my feathery den.
Through the slats it shines
As I've returned to drifty drowse.

To see me well through the day
Pesky demons held at bay;
To this in-between reverie
Splashes my bright grace.

– T. P. Foster

Grace the Boat by Ann Marie Smigelski

Early Morning by Edith Wood

Sophia by Jean-Marie Cote

From Vincent to Arlene

The days they pass so wicked fast
The plans we have so rarely last
A day or two we dream of fun
It passes quickly with the sun.

What lasts is what sustains us so
The bond we formed those years ago
We always know what keeps us strong
It's the love we've shared in the years, now long.

I love you much, my sweetest dear
It's always peaceful when we are near
The bond is strong, the love severe
You will always be my friend, My Queen!

May you always know peace, joy, happiness, good health,
And much patience with the rascal you married.

– Vincent Murphy, written for his wife, Arlene
for Valentine's Day 2006

24

Goodness by Donna Varner

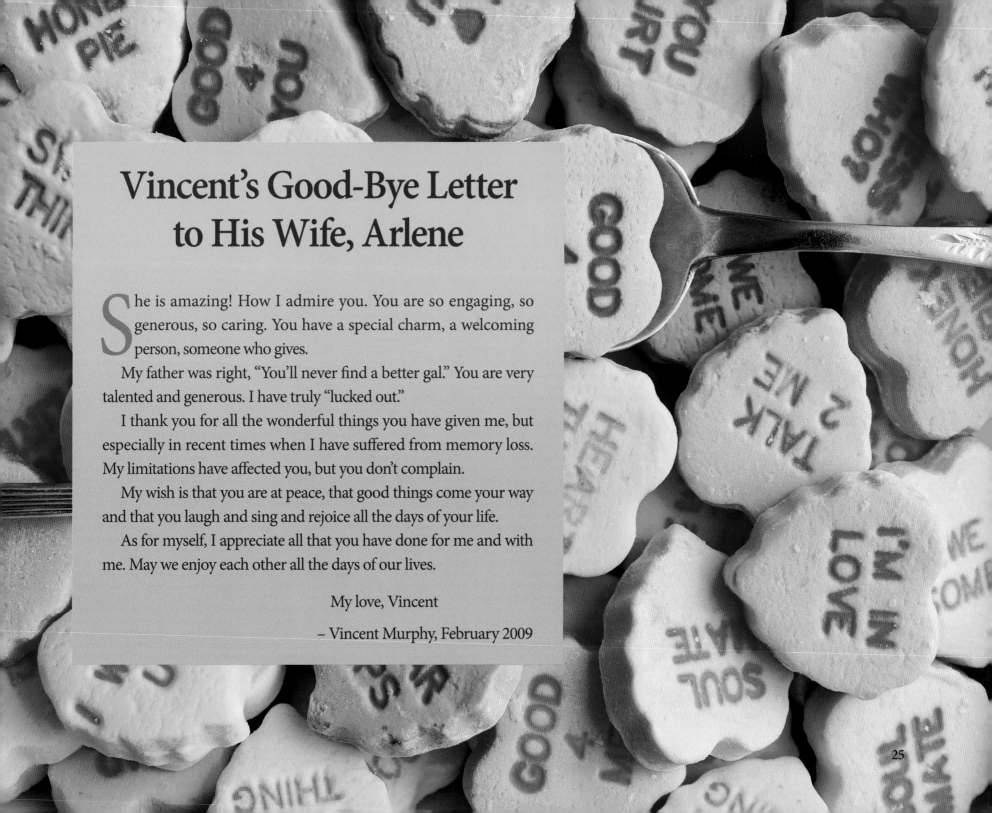

Vincent's Good-Bye Letter to His Wife, Arlene

She is amazing! How I admire you. You are so engaging, so generous, so caring. You have a special charm, a welcoming person, someone who gives.

My father was right, "You'll never find a better gal." You are very talented and generous. I have truly "lucked out."

I thank you for all the wonderful things you have given me, but especially in recent times when I have suffered from memory loss. My limitations have affected you, but you don't complain.

My wish is that you are at peace, that good things come your way and that you laugh and sing and rejoice all the days of your life.

As for myself, I appreciate all that you have done for me and with me. May we enjoy each other all the days of our lives.

My love, Vincent

– Vincent Murphy, February 2009

Meet Me Where I Am

I'm not a zombie, one of the walking dead …
Nor a disposable, yet breathing, paper doll.
I'm still me …
My mind is just a little jumbled,
A bit mixed up.

There's beauty here.
Flashes of the past, clues to the present.
A kaleidoscope of wonder.
Images of a different time and space
Hypnotize and seduce …
Jumbled perhaps, and quite mixed up.

I'm no less creative, no less intelligent.
I really am still me.
My brain is simply wired a little differently now.
Just a little jumbled and a bit mixed up.

Don't discard me, I'm still here.
But your world frightens me.
Can you come to me?
Meet me where I am to laugh, to love, to share.
Visit me here … and excuse the clutter …
It's just a little jumbled and a bit mixed up.

– Edwina Hoyle

Peaceful Repose by Albert Heacox

27

Cute Couple by Edith Wood

The Journey

As long as I can remember
I never looked forward
to going on long trips or
traveling to distant lands.

My brother-in-law relished
traveling throughout
the United States and Canada

But, not me.

My friends would travel to
Australia, China or Africa,
Spending long hours in
planes, trains and buses.

But, not me.

Except in dire necessity
I stayed close to home.

But that all changed.
In the late 1990s
I found myself embarking on
the longest journey
of my life.

It was a trip that
needed no travel agents,
no tickets, no vouchers,
no reservations or schedules
and no planned itineraries.

There were no upgrades
No 1st or 2nd class
accommodations
No special treatment
Everyone was (to coin a phrase)
In the same boat.

It was a journey that
could not be changed
or cancelled.

The suitcases taken on
this journey would not be
packed with clothing or
personal belongings,
but filled with seventy-plus
years of lifetime memories.

And as the trip continued
those memories

slowly disappear.
And when the journey
nears its end,
the cases are empty.
It is similar
to a ship that embarks
from one port but
never finds a friendly
port to disembark.

It's a one-way
flight that
takes off, but
never lands.

When I started on this journey
I didn't hear the words
"See you soon" or
"Until we meet again," but
just a simple
"Good-bye."

The day I came
to realize that
my wife of 50 years
had Alzheimer's was
when the journey began
and
still continues …

– Lindy Lindenbaum

The Road to Heaven by Jean-Marie Cote

Golden Awakening by Edith Wood   31

Who?

Who are you? I can't quite decide.
Are you my protector?
An ever-present sentry charged with my safety?
Like an owl on a branch—visible, but camouflaged.
There to notice, yet hidden in plain sight.

Who are you? I can't quite decide.
Are you my lover, my soulmate?
A keeper of secrets? Guardian of my heart?
So familiar, yet mysterious.
Recognition evaporates like morning fog.

Who are you? I can't quite decide.
Always present, kind of familiar.
A delicious sense of déjà vu
Makes me smile and dance inside.
It is the quest that delights.

Who are you? I can't quite decide.
When the veil lifts and I see you for you,
My heart and spirit soar.
A whisper, a heartbeat, a glimpse … and it's gone.
Who are you? I can't quite decide.

– Edwina Hoyle

Owls by James Hartley Smith

33

Oak Tree in the Marsh by Edith Wood

Mama's Baby

Church of the Daisies by Donna Varner

It was my turn to take Mom to the ladies' room at the restaurant.

As I helped her wash her hands, she noticed the fold-up changing table attached to the wall in the corner.

She dried her hands and said thoughtfully, and with a nod toward the thing, "I'm thinking that is where I put my baby to change his diaper."

"You are exactly right!" I exclaimed. I thought perhaps some of her long-ago memories were resurfacing.

"How many babies do you have?" I asked. She didn't recall.

"Do you know that I am one of your babies?" I asked, knowing I might be disappointed with her answer.

She looked at me with a most quizzical grin and nearly chuckled as she replied, "No, you're not!"

And she was absolutely right.

I was certainly not a baby. I was a full-grown woman, standing here with her in the little diner restroom.

As I glanced in the mirror and saw her face smiling at mine, it didn't matter. We were together, and that was good enough.

– Lynne Cope Hummell

Gullah Hands by Robert Ovelman

Flipped

A fellow caregiver was late for support group. When she arrived she just had to tell us why. On her way, she had stopped at the post office so that her husband could do his daily routine to check the mail.

While turning in from traffic, she got rear-ended and her car flipped over onto the roof! Rather panicked but unhurt, she immediately checked on her husband. He was fine—he had unbuckled his seatbelt, climbed out, and gone into the post office— never even noticing the car was upside down!

That's Alzheimer's for you!

– Jeffra Emmerich

Familiar

The drive was 11 hours so we made some stops on the way. Each time we stopped, Grannie took out her keys. When I asked why she had her keys out, she always said, "Well, we're going home, aren't we?"

Along the way we talked about how she was feeling and what she had been doing at home in Michigan. She kept talking about "Saunnie." She asked me if I know Saunnie. She said, "Saunnie is so good to me. She brings me groceries, takes me to the store, paints my nails and is just a great friend."

After we stopped at Becky's for the night, we continued on the next day to see her sister, Rubena. It was a wonderfully happy reunion, seeing not only her sister, but other cousins and an old friend.

That evening, Grannie sat in the living room of Rubena's house with her keys in her hands. I asked her why she had her keys out, and she said, "We're going home, aren't we?"

She also said she didn't know where she was and that she wanted to go home. I told her that the next morning we would go home.

That morning we were having breakfast in the kitchen and again she asked me if I knew that wonderful friend of hers, Saunnie.

I then said, "Grannie, I'm Saunnie."

She said, "I thought you looked familiar."

– Sandee Brooks

A Glimpse

"Our friends are here," he says, but of course our names elude him.

On our beach walks the topic we have left is whatever is before us—the color of the water or the crazy running of the birds. So on the deck, Vinny and I are not making a lot of profound or un-profound sense.

Suddenly he looks toward me and says, "But how are you?"

For a moment his presence deepens, there is some kind of visitation, and then he is gone again, gone away.

I love the glimpse and remember with love the years of our connection.

– Jane Litzinger

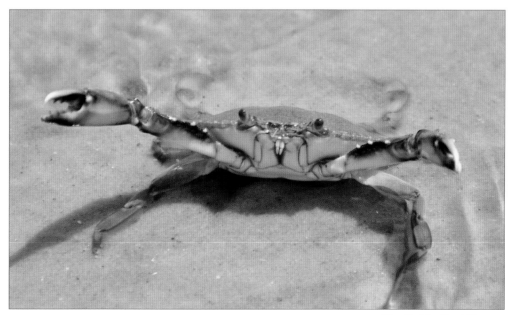

Blue Crab by Carol Clemens

Tide Marks by Edith Wood

The Work of Memory Matters

FREE, CONFIDENTIAL MEMORY SCREENINGS

Are you concerned about changes in your memory? Do you have trouble concentrating?

Do you have trouble recalling words or names in conversation? Memory screenings are a significant first step to determine if there is a problem.

For those concerned about memory loss, or those experiencing warning signs of dementia, there are benefits to early detection. Memory screenings are free and confidential, and appointments are required.

BOOST YOUR BRAINPOWER

Brain Boosters is an extraordinary 10-week class for anyone in the community who wants to maintain a healthy brain. With up to 500 trillion synaptic connections, your brain

is easily the most powerful machine in the world. These connections create your thoughts, drive your emotions, and control your behavior. Your brain is constantly changing through a process known as "brain plasticity," so you can improve and enhance your brain's jaw-dropping powers at any age!

While it was traditionally thought that our brains were fully formed by adulthood, the truth is that our life experiences continually shape and mold our brains in fascinating ways.

With every new problem you solve, and every new insight or skill you learn, you strengthen a range of functions involved in brain fitness. There is power in lifelong learning. Challenge yourself! Brain Boosters teaches the facts about brain health in a fun, educational environment.

MAKING CONNECTIONS

Connections is a weekly program designed for those in the early stages of dementia or who have mild cognitive impairment. Connections empowers participants to take

control of their diagnosis and helps them avoid being defined by their diagnosis. Those with early memory loss deserve the highest quality services to address memory changes. Connections is a proactive program that encourages cognitive stimulation using technology designed to improve visual, language, memory and spatial skills.

The program also incorporates yoga and meditation to help promote a sense of well-being. Participants experience success, increased confidence and self-esteem in this challenging, yet failure-free environment in which the activities purposefully focus on maintaining and strengthening current abilities.

THE CLUB

The Club is a Social Day Program that offers a safe, confidential, failure-free zone for those diagnosed with Alzheimer's or other forms of dementia. Activities are designed to stimulate socialization, laughter and remembrances while caregivers have a chance to recharge their batteries.

Our program is exciting, cutting-edge and uses software with over 4,000 activity programs. This technology allows our "armchair travelers" to visit Rome, Paris, or Greece with the click of a button. We can zero in on childhood neighborhoods using Google Earth. Imagine the conversations that take place when tapping into these long-term memories. Art and music are used to stimulate creative expression and yoga enriches their sense of wellbeing.

Our club members are never left alone or excluded. Our staff knows the specific needs of each participant and the current challenges the family faces.

All club members are cared for without embarrassment or degradation and we focus on abilities (not disabilities) and successes (not failures).

CARE FOR THE CAREGIVER

Caregiving is a labor of love. Memory Matters offers relief to families because we know how the stress of caregiving impacts physical and emotional health. When your world is changing and you don't know what to do or what to expect, Memory Matters helps navigate these rough waters.

Caregivers are encouraged to join support groups to connect with others who are experiencing the same life-changing role. We offer several support groups including specialized groups for both men and women. We offer individual counseling and confidentiality is always respected.

OUR HISTORY

In 1997 our organization was founded as a grassroots, non-profit organization called Alzheimer's Respite & Resource (AR&R). Our name has changed, but our mission and our commitment to serve the families in our community who need our help remains steadfast. In 2009 we completed the construction of our permanent home and Memory Matters became our new name.

843-842-6688 office
info@memory-matters.org

The Power of Art

"We are all born with natural abilities for creativity and art. Often as we 'grow up' we lose sight of our creative, artistic selves. For the person with dementia, finding that creative self again can be life-changing. For the caregiver it can mean moments of fun and joy."

– Cathee Stegall, artist and Memory Matters program director

Barb B., MM participant

Art gives a voice to those with dementia. As dementia progresses, cognitive abilities decline, making it a struggle to complete sentences, to find words, and express emotions causing a heightened feeling of failure and loss of self-worth. Through art therapy, clients receive the gift of self-expression, an unheard voice to their emotions, and the opportunity to be successful, to be engaged in meaningful activity, and to feel a sense of accomplishment. Many non-verbal clients "come to life" when a paint brush is put in their hands. They can "tell their story" through art.

Jackie K., MM participant

Jane P., MM participant

Florence O., MM participant

Sara B., MM participant

Bev D., MM volunteer

Ruth A., MM participant

Shelia B., MM volunteer

Sarah D., MM participant

Cathee Stegall, MM program director

Peg K., MM volunteer

Bob H., MM participant

Sierra, MM participant

George S., MM participant

Art is an activity designed to unlock one's creative expression, reduce anxiety, frustration and stress, lift depression and increase self-esteem.

The person with dementia may not remember the next day that they even painted anything … but at the moment of creation, they felt energized and had expression. One of the benefits of doing an art project with someone is a feeling of teamwork and accomplishment. Keep in mind, the result may not be perfect … it's the expression that matters. Give it a try. The only drawback is making a mess—but sometimes cleaning up together can be just as fun.

Art takes many forms: self-portraits using acrylics on canvas; memory collages using old photographs, lace, buttons and other embellishments; beautiful watercolor paintings like imitations of the great artists such as Monet and Renoir; and even simple craft projects. At Memory Matters the art produced throughout the year is exhibited at an annual fundraising event. Our clients are incredibly proud that the sale of their art supports their "club."

Sarah D., MM participant

Tanya G., MM participant

Sonia B., MM participant

Jane P., MM participant

Lorrayne H., MM participant

Lorrayne H., MM participant

Lorrayne H., MM participant

Lorrayne H., MM participant

Lorrayne H., MM participant

Lorrayne H., MM participant

Art featured on this page is by Lorrayne Harris, a participant who had studied fashion illustration.

Juanita W., MM participant

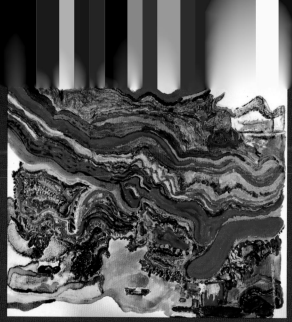
Marshall M., MM participant

Marshall M., a Memory Matters participant and former geologist. Note that his landscape is painted as a topographical map.

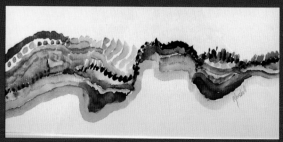
Marshall M., MM participant

Bob H., MM participant

Francis H., MM participant

Vivian F., MM participant

Ruth F., MM participant

George H., MM participant

George H., MM volunteer

Ed S., MM participant

Jack S., MM participant

Swans in Love by Fran Baer

Her Presence

I see her face in the moon's reflection on the water;
I feel her touch as soft warm breezes move across my body;
I hear her voice in the silence of the night;
Her beauty continually surrounds me.

– Larry Davidson

High Summer by Donna Varner

Rays of Hope by Guy Kriske

When Memories Matter: Finding Hope and Humor in Dementia

Daddy doesn't play the organ any more.

He has hammered out Bible songs on the piano and organ since I can remember. He took piano lessons growing up and always lamented that he didn't practice enough as a child, like his sister, Mary.

We all thought it was good for Daddy to play the organ in his later years, especially after dementia started to slowly steal him away.

Other things have left him in recent years. Many of you know how this process works. He was glad to see my sister on a recent prolonged visit. But at one point he asked her, "Now what's your maiden name?"

He still likes to read aloud, carefully enunciating each word and announcing the commas and new paragraphs.

He can still pray. And he recites the blessing that was always used before meals in his childhood.

In the early stages, Daddy was given medication. Mama made sure he took it every morning. And every morning, Daddy would say, "What's this for?"

And every morning, she would say: "It's for your memory, George."

When this process started, everyone said we needed to tend to my mother, his caregiver.

Following the advice of several veterans, I ordered her a copy of *The 36-Hour Day: A Family Guide to Caring for Persons with Alzheimer's Disease, Related Dementing Illnesses, and Memory Loss in Later Life.*

She had already been given a bag full of helpful books, which she did not have time to read. And besides, Daddy just moved them around the house so it was hard to keep up with them.

– David Lauderdale

The Dance of Life

My brother, Joel, had been a child psychologist who worked hard to get his patients on track while giving them psychological tests to determine their mental acuity. A big turning point in the progression of his disease was the horror of being given similar tests to determine how damaged his brain was at the tender age of 70.

Results of many tests indicated that he probably suffered from Lewy Body disease.

During one visit in the facility, I talked with him about our teenage years when we used to dance together. His reaction was immediate, positive and animated.

Not only did his eyes light up and twinkle, but there was again a big smile and a yearning to get up and dance down the facility hallways. And dance we did!

It was the cha-cha that really got his hips gyrating as he moved ever so gently, imitating Fred Astaire's rhythmic movements. We laughed so hard until we collapsed on the sofa.

I vividly remember the smiles on some of the nurses' faces as well as the caregivers who, although mired in their own pain, looked up, smiled, and perhaps a tear or two slid down their cheeks.

– Shirley Alberti

When I look in the mirror I don't know who's looking at me

I'm not at all sure whose reflection I see

Whose eyes, whose nose, whose mouth, whose chin

Where do I end and where do I begin.

I used to know who is me, but now I'm not sure anymore.

– Bonnie Evans

Seas of Change by Guy Kriske

Remember When by Nancy Huntington

Aways There

For most of my life, I took my mother for granted. She was always there for me, emotionally, physically, financially, socially, mentally … just always there.

However, when she began to experience memory loss, I also felt a sense of loss. My mother was no longer always there.

Soon the tables turned and my mother needed me to be there for her … to pay bills, provide transport, and perform miscellaneous daily duties. However, one day I realized that although I was there with my mother physically, I was not really WITH her. I needed to change!

Rather than speaking AT my mother, I began to talk WITH her. It no longer mattered that she could not remember what she had for breakfast or the day's date. What mattered was where she was in time, what her mind was disclosing that day, and what SHE remembered. No more daily quizzes or instructions … just talking, smiling and even laughing.

Viewing old photographs together opened up a whole new dialogue. Her memory took me to places of her youth, experiences that I had never heard about and to people I had never known.

Although I could not validate the accuracy of her recollections, the journey was exhilarating.

Seeing her beautiful smile as she glanced into this briefly open window in her mind was priceless.

I am forever grateful to God for allowing me that time to be there for my mother. Now my cherished memories are always there, warming my heart.

– Beverly Dlouhy

Music of the Mind

My grandmother, Laura Lindenbaum, was a brilliant student, talented pianist and concert cellist. I remember watching her practice piano for hours on end, working diligently to master her song selection.

She had so many talents, hobbies and collections that she never ceased to amaze me.

She had been showing signs of Alzheimer's for years when my parents moved from New York to South Carolina. I was 7.

It took only two years for my grandmother to reach the next stage of Alzheimer's. She began to wander. She seemed distant and detached.

But she never seemed to give up on the piano. I think it was her only constant. The keys were always the same and the notes always meant the same rhythmic pattern.

In my younger years, I had looked up to my grandmother's playing with admiration. Now I saw it as desperation. She no longer played for pleasure and fun. Each note she played was, to me, another attempt to grab the fleeting memories that floated away.

My grandpa never wanted to put her into a home, but he knew it was time. I went to visit almost every day.

There was a piano in the Alzheimer's wing and, of course, my grandmother gravitated to it. But her one source of comfort soon slipped away. It was as if when the music left, so did the rest of her mind.

I was in ninth grade when my grandmother's battle was over. I like to think she won it and it was just her time to go.

Actually, I know she won it. That was the kind of person she was.

– Holli Selman

One morning when Gert came out of the bedroom wearing her dress backwards, her husband Karl said, "Gert, I see you got ready by yourself today, but your dress is on backwards."

She replied, "That's okay. I'll just turn around."

Another time when Gert was merrily playing the piano like she was giving a concert, Karl asked, "Gertie, why are you playing so happily?"

She answered, "I'm playing for the audience"—meaning the rows of framed pictures on top of the piano.

– Denise Isacson

Mountain Morning Fog by Fran Baer

Still   When we walk in the sun, there remains the golden glisten as the rays pass through her hair. As I pull her close there remains the sweet fragrance of her hair. There remains the purposeful soft caress of her hand on my arm. There remains the touch of her hands on my body wanting to hold on—clinging to maintain the feel.

Still she pulls me up off the couch, still calls my antics stupid even in a whisper, and yes, she can still make me laugh.

All is not lost.

– Larry Davidson

Escapees

I was a "newbie" in the dementia-care world. I had less than a month on the job when the program director went on vacation. Suddenly, a dozen clients in our respite day program were my responsibility.

It was definitely scary and intimidating —not only was I new, but the site of the program was a church hall that had multiple exits. Those with dementia wander, right?

Head-counting became my obsession. I had to ensure there were no escapees! On my third day, during one of my compulsive counts, a sense of absolute panic washed over me. I was missing two people. And frankly, I couldn't even figure out who they were! I asked my volunteers to make sure that NO ONE left the room while I began a search.

Then I remembered Ginny, a flamboyant 80-year-old former Broadway actress who loved her bright red lipstick. I had been warned that she frequently managed to sneak cigarettes into the program. After lunch she would often ask to sit in the courtyard … hmmm.

"That may account for one of the missing clients," I thought. So I sprinted to the courtyard door. Thank goodness it was an enclosed space without access to the street. I pushed the door open in a panic, and there was Ginny puffing away on her Virginia Slims cigarette. Bingo!

To my surprise, Miss Betty was with her. She, too, had a cigarette! Standing with one hand on her hip and the other holding the cigarette in a glamorous, bus-stop pose, she reminded me of Greta Garbo or Lauren Bacall in an old black-and-white movie.

I marched over to her and scolded her saying, "Miss Betty, give me that cigarette!"

She defiantly stepped back and demanded, "Why?"

"Because you don't smoke!" I responded.

Wide-eyed confusion spread over her face. She looked at the Virginia Slim in her hand and said, "I don't??"

– Edwina Hoyle

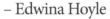

by Lorrayne H., MM participant

Support Groups ...
Do it For You

It's the evening I look forward to each month with both anticipation and dread. What will I hear that will tug at my heart and bring the tears that lie so close to the surface?

It is the night of my Alzheimer's support group meeting. It's a group of people like me, caregivers.

From these understanding people, we each learn, find support, share stories, share frustrations, share the small triumphs and share our loss. Knowing that I have this group of caring people, I feel less alone in my role as caregiver.

I know I have friends to whom I can turn when new situations arise. Someone will have an answer. Someone has been there and can offer help and a sympathetic ear.

My Alzheimer's support group is one of the best things I do for myself, and thus my mother. We both benefit from my involvement.

– Mary Dempsey

A Consociation by Chandler Hummell

The Lasting Gift

Ella Kaplan and granddaughter Ella Brooke Simons

My grandmother, Ella Kaplan, had Alzheimer's disease. She embodied grace and led by example in teaching us to be kind and loving.

It was hard watching her memory decline. The woman who everyone adored felt alone when she couldn't remember that we visited regularly and called as often as we could.

But in 2003, I was able to give her a gift that seemed to light a spark inside her fading mind. When our daughter was born, we named her Ella Brooke, in my grandmother's honor. While she couldn't remember family events, names, or what she did two hours before, she never forgot this gift we gave to her.

In the 10 months between my daughter's birth and my grandmother's death, every time I called or visited, the first thing my Nana would say when she heard my voice was "Ella Brooke, 7 pounds, 7 ounces, right?"

"Yes, Nana." Then I would think to myself, "I don't know how, but you remembered."

– Elise Silver Simons

Fresh Flowers Every Day

"*Five foot two, eyes of blue, but oh what those five feet could do! Has anybody seen my gal? ...*" Betty shuffles over to the vinyl-topped, folding card table wearing her typical Tuesday garb, an electric yellow outfit in a bold flamingo and palm tree print.

To quell Betty's restlessness and boost her self-esteem, we begin every day with an elementary yet engaging activity —clipping images from magazines. Betty's baby blue eyes, reddened from the blood-thinning medication prescribed to slow the progression of her dementia, stare blankly at the tall stack of garden magazines on the table.

"*Don't sit under the apple tree with anyone else but me ... *" As she cups the scissors in her wrinkled hands, she looks at me expectantly, awaiting instructions on what they are for. I am dumbfounded that this talented woman, who has regaled me with the details of sewing her own wedding gown, cannot remember how to use the tools of her trade.

Sensing Betty's apprehension and discomfort, I transform this meaningless activity by telling her it is a special project that only she is skilled enough to perform. Detailed instructions and constant encouragement and praise are the easily provided catalysts that allow Betty to successfully complete the project and glow with pleasure.

"*Eastside, Westside, all around the town ... *" As I watch Betty proudly circle the room, showing off her handiwork, I appreciate that her disease has not yet crippled her ability to express and understand emotion. I overlook the trivial nature of this kindergarten-level activity, realizing the feelings of value and self-worth it has provided Betty.

Tossing the flower images into the garbage at the end of the day, I know we will happily create a fresh batch tomorrow.

– Heather Black

(Heather Black is a student at Duke University who volunteered at AR&R, now Memory Matters, for several summers. She wrote this essay as part of her college entrance application.)

Memories

Summer slips through the

Branches of the tree

To the hard ground

Of winter.

The taste of wild berries

Lingers on our lips,

As does our love,

Now as quiet as

A blanket of snow.

– Art Cornell

Where I'm From

I'm from a lost memory somewhere in his mind
From my grandfather I call Papa who is so sweet and kind
I am from a 90-year-old man who doesn't know my name
From the time I was eight until today my name, Harrison,
    has slipped away

I'm from the kindest person in the world
From never knowing what to say or what to think

I'm from I wish he knew that I'm ten years old
    and growing up before his eyes
From family pictures and videos, I can
remember the sweet memories of the past

I'm from I wish he knew that I'm his grandson
    and not his son
From he gives you hugs and kisses no matter who you are
And forever grateful that he is in my life.

– Harrison L., age 10

Umbrella Line Up by Karen Migliaccio

Buddies by Fran Baer

Being Here Now

When visiting the memory care center, I was able to see the effects of dementia first-hand. To see these people not able to remember parts of their own life or remember words was heartbreaking. It is one thing to read about Alzheimer's, but to actually see one man forget if he even liked pizza was something else entirely.

Each of their lives were so interesting, but they could not remember much about their own lives … all of the things they saw, heard, laughed and cried about. It made me so thankful for the moment I am in.

To make myself feel like everything was all right, I told myself: "This is making these people happy right now. It doesn't matter that I am not able to make a difference in the future. All that matters is that for one, brief moment, they are happy."

For that one moment, I made them happy and relaxed. I made a difference in the moment.

I made a motto for myself a few years ago. I remembered it again when I saw these people. I have been through so much throughout my life that I started "living every minute of every day." The reason I remembered this motto is because all of these people must live the same way. They could not live in the past. They could not live in the future. They must live every minute of every day. They didn't start to live this way by their own decision. The disease forced them into it.

I will forever try to live like them, laughing and enjoying every minute of every day.

– Nate Anderson, age 17

This was written as a class assignment after visiting Memory Matters. At the time it was written, Nate was afflicted with Guillain-Barre Syndrome and he was able to draw from his own experience dealing with health issues to discover parallels between himself and those afflicted with dementia.

Everyone With One

Everyone with a loved one, friend, or acquaintance with Alzheimer's has stories of heartbreak and sadness, but we also have stories of humor and compassion. I remember one of the last Thanksgivings at home with my sister Hilda. The family was gathered in a circle, holding hands and we were asked to say one thing we were thankful for during this time of year. We all said the usual things and when we got to my sister, she said, "I'm just not into this." A hearty laugh went up all around and my sister gave a big smile at our response.

– Joy Isaacs

In loving memory of my sister Hilda Deekins who passed away last April after living 14 years with Alzheimer's.

Dandelion by Donna Varner

A brilliant mind, a beautiful soul,

Stolen away from one not so old.

Anticipating the future,

And mourning his loss,

These are his words that we came across.

– Marshall Stuart Miller
three years before entering an Alzheimer's community

Inner Beauty Expressed

There is a quiet-natured gentleman in our program who prefers to spend his time working on puzzles and drawings, distanced from the other members of our "club." According to his family, this has always been the man's character, although Alzheimer's has seemingly amplified his introversion.

Perhaps it is because of this that the effect of connecting with him in hushed conversation makes me feel like I have been granted admission to a secret society.

One day, the gentleman was finishing a colored pencil drawing. I paused and commented on his beautiful piece of art before teasing, "There's not any chance that one is for me?"

He replied with a smile, "This is for my wife." Sure enough, I later saw him giving the picture to his bride of over 50 years before we all left Memory Matters for a long holiday weekend.

The following week I noticed he was working on another drawing. "How lovely!" I said. "Your drawing is for me, right?"

He smoothly replied, "No, this one is for my wife. But," he said, pulling a finished, autographed drawing from underneath his project, "this one is for you."

Not only had my friend recalled our last exchange a week earlier and had the forethought to complete a project with his signature, but he had found a way to give of himself on his own terms.

I immediately posted his artwork on my office wall, for the beauty it possesses reaches far beyond the bold strokes of color. Besides, it is an overt confirmation of my admittance into this special man's secret society.

– Ashley Gruber

by George Simpson, MM participant

Joy and Compassion on Four Legs

Dogs are truly man's (and woman's) best friend. At the "club," we are very fortunate to have pet therapy often. When the dogs arrive, the participants are immediately engaged. Some talk to the dogs, calling them the name of a former dog they owned. There are hugs, laughing—and some howling!—and a sense of familiarity and warmth engulfs the room.

One of the special dogs is Joy. I met her as a little two-year old Beagle, when I worked for a residence that included a memory neighborhood. Joy was scheduled to be euthanized if a home was not found. She found a home at the residence.

Joy had the instinct and compassion of a human caregiver. If she heard someone crying, she would go sit by that person, head in her lap, and soon the resident was petting her soft head. Almost immediately a sense of calmness would take over.

Joy would curl up in front of the TV when friends were gathered to watch "The Price is Right." In short, she became part of the family.

As time went on, the population in the dementia neighborhood changed and many of the residents died. Joy became very sad and did not understand the changes. New people came and the staff did not have time for Joy. There were days when she was not walked or taken outdoors. She gave so much love, and needed love in return.

Joy the dog

The first thing I would do in the morning when I got to work was to go visit Joy. She would race down the hall, howling, ears flapping, and would literally jump into my arms. We would do a little dance together and I would take her for a walk. I started taking her home on the weekends, then evenings, and finally when I left that job, Joy came home with me.

This special girl is now 14 years old, happy and the most loving dog you will ever meet. She now has a sister, Girly Girl, who came to us through a foster home.

Joy continues to do with her own family and our neighborhood as she did with the people in the dementia center: She loves everyone … and I love her.

– Karen Doughtie

Father, I Need Your Help

Precious Father, I need your help this morning. There is so much that I want to do today for my special friends.

As I take their wrinkled hands in mine, keep me mindful of the many important and useful things these hands have done. They have cared for infants and children, fought in wars, built bridges, started companies.

They have created beautiful art, planted and harvested fields and gardens, and caressed a spouse. They have bandaged knees and styled hair, cooked meals and fixed cars.

There are far too many things to name … but You know them all, God.

Keep me mindful. Let my hands be warm and welcoming and give them confidence that they are in a safe place.

Lord, I pray that for these hours, I can erase the isolation they might feel from their disease, and replace it with stimulation and fun and laughter. I so want their time with us to be one of sharing the simple joys of being with caring friends. My hope is that through creative ways, we can exercise their minds and bodies and let them experience the joys of their yesterdays through song, dance, and activities they will enjoy.

I want them to experience unbridled laughter … that is so good for the soul.

Lord, let our words always be affirming and encouraging. Let their experience with us never be one of frustration. Let it always be one of uplifting and success.

Let our hugs be tender and loving, and our smiles be smiles from our hearts.

Lord, I pray that our time with our friends is a light in their tangled and confusing world. And when we hug them good-bye at the end of the day, we know it was a day well spent doing Your will.

Thank you, Lord, always for your amazing love for us. I am so thankful to know that you have your gentle arms securely around them … my dear friends … as they leave us until tomorrow.

In Your precious and holy name. Amen.

– Trish Elliott

Outstretched Ams by R. W. Daley

Memory of My Mother

My mother and I did not have a close relationship. Sadly, this continued throughout our lives.

But a strange and wonderful thing happened as she became older and began to slip further into dementia.

Years earlier I had ceased to use my childhood given name and had chosen to be called "Beth." Throughout this time I called her often, introducing myself as "Beth, from Atlanta." I often would fly or drive to Indianapolis as my sister, niece and I continued to try to find the situation that was right for her. I always introduced myself to my mother as "Beth, from Atlanta."

She was soon calling me "Beth, that sweet lady from Atlanta," and she and I were able to have, for a couple of years, that sweet, loving relationship I had always desired.

As she continued to drift further away, eventually not recognizing any of us, God continued to be merciful. Mother had always distrusted strangers and could have a biting tongue.

Then she was given her mantra. It was "I love you."

To all the workers and helpers, her fellow travelers in the Alzheimer's ward, all guests, it was a continual "I love you."

My sister, niece and I would laugh. It so easily could have been something else.

– Elizabeth Haverfield

by Cathee Stegall

68

Giving Back a Little Love

Every time my grandmother sees me, she holds out her right pinkie for our secret handshake. We lock our pinkies, shake our hands back and forth while murmuring the accompanying chant, and then throw our hands in the air and yell "Wooh!"

I can't tell you the words; they're obviously a tip-top secret.

We created this handshake when I was 8 and still went to "Mimi Camp," a week out of every summer when I stayed at my grandparents' house.

Even as my grandmother is beginning to forget street names and the time of day, even though she can't drive herself to water aerobics anymore, and even though she has stopped being able to bake lemon love-notes and shortbread cookies, she remembers to hold out her pinkie and dance with me, every time we see each other.

> *I am truly blessed to have a wonderful wife for so many years and a wonderful family that supports us.*
> *She is the love of my life.*
> *She is the mother of two beautiful children.*
> *She is the grandmother of six beautiful grandchildren.*
> *She is always a lady.*
> *She is a loving and giving person.*
> *She is a college graduate and a mother.*
>
> – Barry Payne

Mimi used to take me to the pool and wait for hours—literally up to seven hours—while I played "shadow mermaid." She taught me how to golf, and when I didn't hit the ball within 20 tries, how to laugh it off and go shopping instead.

Even though my grandmother is incredibly polite and conservative, she recognized my outdoor instincts and nurtured them by telling me stories about rabbits and fairies who live in the woods. She never became upset when I came skipping home covered in mud.

Alzheimer's has taken a lot from my family, but we have learned a lot as well. Instead of becoming bitter or upset, Mimi just giggles when her memory slips and she can't think of a word.

She has taught my whole family that it's possible, and often best, to laugh when times are worst. We work together like I have never seen before.

Personally, I have learned that when I can't fix something, it doesn't mean I have failed. It just means that the solution isn't apparent yet, or maybe is not what I think it is.

I can't cure Alzheimer's right now, but I can sit with Mimi for an hour and paint her nails and we can laugh about my boy trouble. I can't help my mom with her grief, but I can wash the dishes so she has one less thing to worry about.

There's always a way to give a little love back.

– Sophia McPheeters Navarre

Solomon Said It

"Something is wrong with my teeth. Something is not right. Nothing hurts, but it's just not right." So began our day ... every day.

We had taken Mom to two local dentists and she was given a clean bill of health from both. Dr. Abrams suggested having Mom rinse with salt and water. Dr. Langer said to try a new, soft-bristle toothbrush. Still the complaints went on.

I decided to try one more dentist, Dr. Solomon. He told me that he had experienced this before with Alzheimer's patients. They sometimes get obsessed over something and can't let it go. He, too, agreed that all was clinically well.

When we got home, we talked about the exam and I again explained that the dentist, Dr. Solomon, said nothing was wrong with her teeth.

She looked at me and said, "Well, if Solomon, the wisest man in the Bible said it, it must be true."

I never heard about her teeth again.

– Mary Dempsey

Hands by Art Cornell

Wishes and Hopes

I wish he could kiss me and tell me he loves me.

I wish he was still with me.

I hope he doesn't suffer.

I hope money doesn't become a problem.

I hope he dies before I do.

I am lonely without him, but healthy.

I am a strong woman.

I am fortunate to have married him.

– Anonymous

I wish I could hear Jim laugh.

I am going to heal with the help of family and friends.

He is still with me.

– Lis Jones

I hope I can accept the new "normal."

I am overwhelmed, angry, heartbroken.

I remember our life before—laughing together, making plans for the future.

I remember my friend.

– Nancy O'Hara

I miss snuggling.

He is still loveable.

They remember smiling faces.

– Mary Ellen McConnell

I hope he understands I did my best.

He was passionate.

He remembers music and rhythms, but not words.

He doesn't remember all that we did together for over forty-four years.

– Jeffra Emmerich

I wish there was a cure for Alzheimer's.

I am determined to meet my responsibilities head on in assisting her.

She is trying as hard as anyone to meet her challenges.

I am trying to do the same, with patience and determination.

– John Goff

Just a Thought

Does one's faith have a role in Alzheimer's disease caregiving?

There is no denying that caring for a loved one with Alzheimer's disease is one of life's most frustrating and demanding challenges. Caregiver stress and exhaustion are ever present and physical health is challenged. Respite and daycare programs and help at home are quite useful, but the fundamental problem remains.

Isolation can be progressive. The Alzheimer's disease

Gathering Storm, oil painting, by Charles P. Duvall

blogs are full of specific laments and unsolvable problems.

"Pray," many suggest.

Indeed, faith can be the needed wind beneath sagging wings. The stronger the faith, the more dedicated the quest for more complete discipleship, the more meaningful and full the support can be. In caregiving one must be gentle and kind. One must always remember the patient will more likely respond to goodness than the opposite.

Faithfulness not only to God but to the loved one is rather fundamental. The repeated frustrations call for strong self control.

Above all else, the most critical personal value becomes patience. That's a pretty good job description for the successful Alzheimer's disease caregiver.

Those values just happen also to be the Fruits of the Spirit (Galatians 5:22-23). With growing faith and a deepening relationship with Jesus Christ, these fruits become more abundant and more sweet.

This can result in true joy, deepening love and an overall sense of peace, despite the indescribably challenging situation at hand. These last three boons are also Fruits of the Spirit.

Just a thought—make that a prayer—for you.

– Charles P. Duvall, MD

Love Complete

On days such as this,
sky-piercing blue,
White wisps float;
Love is the whole and
more than all, much more.

Shared moments—
surf crashing, rays heating,
sand clinging—
Futures to dream, capsules of
time remembered,
Looking at the music of
our lives,
And love is the whole
and more than all,
much more.

Give me your hand once
more before this day's
night begins.
Your gentle eyes bright, a
touch soft, your voice
my soul vibrates,
And love is the whole
and more than all,
much more.

— Art Cornell

Don't Push! by Edith Wood

Soothed by a Song

After five challenging years, we could no longer keep my mother safely at home and regretfully had to relinquish her care to those who were more able at a nursing home. We would often go, sometimes together, bringing our hugs and smiles, hiding our tears, still singing our songs, as she drifted farther and farther away.

But even when she didn't know us anymore, curled in a fetal position in her cot, she would smile when she heard our music.

One afternoon, I propped her up in a wheelchair and we roamed the halls, me singing a rousing rendition of "O Sole Mio" in a trilling falsetto, trying to amuse her or get some sort of response. As we passed a litter in the hallway where an ancient man reclined, seemingly comatose and very far away, I thanked my stars that my mother had not yet reached that point.

As we passed, a soaring baritone joined in my song. There was no one else but the three of us in that long dark hallway.

I realized that the music was coming from the man on the litter. My song had somehow reached the depths of his soul and brought him back, if only for a little while, to this world.

Although it is endlessly painful, always remember that there is someone there, locked away in the depths of some faraway place, and that sometimes music is the key to bringing them back—if only just for a fleeting moment—to hold our hearts once more.

– Susan R. Safranek

Sonnet for a Last Dance

The retired judge, a widower and avid barbershop
tenor, dutifully came once a month to sing
with the twenty-odd ladies of the Alzheimer's ward.
But only a few ever joined in. The rest just sat,
chin on chest, slumped in their wheelchairs.
Until one day he said: Let's all sing
the Anniversary Waltz. Then one head
did look up. One who had not
moved before, stood and slowly walked
towards him, arms outstretched.
He grasped the cold bony fingers in his hands
and began to waltz around and around; and,
although it never happened again, when they
were done, the mouthed words came: I love you.

– George Young, MD

Happy Dance by Carol Clemens

Grandpa

February 28, 1901 – September 22, 1987

There he sat.

Time had reduced
His once overwhelming stature
To a miniature mockery
Of his legendary self.

As a child
Full of wild imagination
I lived his ancient stories
Of horse-drawn steam-driven
Fire engines pounding down
The streets of Cleveland.

The proud Fireman Captain
Battling the oil slick fires
Of the Cuyahoga River

The granite hands
Enlarged to grotesque size
By years of duty
And bitter winter frostbite.

Those same hands
Which drew me to his lap
And embraced me
With all the tenderness
Of the Virgin Mary
Cradling her gift.

Now the years
Had removed my name
From his memory.

Some cobweb prevented
Recognition of our connection
But he nodded in strange
Sad smiling remembrance
Of a dream
Long, long ago.
Those distant brown eyes
Flickered for a nagging moment
As he called me
His special friend.

"Where have you been
Since I last saw you … ?
Gosh."
And a shake of his head.
In our final departure

I took those giant hands
And said "I love you."

With a downward glance
Then eye to eye, he said
"Our hands, they're …
They're very compatible."

The seed of my existence
One womb removed
Smiled one last time.

And turned to retire
To the land of horse-drawn
Fire engines
And battles on the Cuyahoga

The boy is Grandfather
of the Father.

And there lives my grandpa.

— Dennis Merrill Bartels

Magnificent Entrance by Robert Ovelman

Clint's Quotes
Clinton Robert Scharff, Jr., age 94

After seeing his granddaughter (age 34) and her husband come in from the beach, Clint turned to his caretaker and said, "Who are these free-loaders anyway? They're eating all my cookies and drinking all my booze!"

One of the cats got outside and I said that he now has dirty feet. Clint turned to Tux and said: "You can't help having dirty feet; you don't have any shoes!"

Acknowledgments

The vision for this book was conceived by a small group of caregivers. Their goal was to showcase the positive aspects of caregiving … joy, love, compassion and humor. Their hope is to inspire others who face the daily challenges of caring for someone with dementia. They also spearheaded this initiative with the objective of "giving back" to Memory Matters, a non-profit organization where each of them found respite, resources and support. For their vision and commitment we wish to publicly acknowledge and thank Jeffra Emmerich, Bonnie Evans, Sharon Miller and Nancy O'Hara.

We are also extremely grateful to the Alzheimer's Foundation of America, The Imlay Foundation and Lynn and John DeZeeuw for providing the funding to underwrite the production and publication costs of this book.

We also thank professional journalist and editor Lynne Cope Hummell and her editorial team: Lauri Allenbach, Lynn DeZeeuw, and Lindy Lindenbaum for their time, commitment and pursuit of excellence. And of course, we are deeply appreciative to publisher Lydia Inglett, an award-winning publisher of elegant books. The professional expertise and wisdom of this team enhanced the project by adding a richness and depth. This is a wonderful example of how a small but powerful group of people with a shared vision can achieve miracles.

Our hope is that you enjoy and treasure this book.

– Edwina Hoyle
Executive Director, Memory Matters

Wheels of Fortune by Vicki Reilly

Contributors